A catalogue record for this book is available
from the British Library

Published by Ladybird Books Ltd
27 Wrights Lane, London, W8 ST2
A Penguin Company

LADYBIRD and the device of a Ladybird are trademarks of
Ladybird Books Ltd

Printed in Great Britain by Butler & Tanner Ltd, Frome

© Disney MCMXCIX

Inspired by Walt Disney Pictures' and Pixar Animation Studios' **A Bug's Life**

Disney • PIXAR

a bug's life

THE BUGTASTIC GUIDE

A Bug's Life is the wonderful story of a tiny world with a big problem... grasshoppers. Ant Island's ant colony is being bullied by a gang led by Hopper, the one-eyed grasshopper. The gang visit the colony every year to demand their food offering. But this year things are different. Hopper wants double the order of food and the ant colony is in danger of starving.

Only one ant, Flik, and
his brave ideas can save
them. But first he must
find some big bugs to help
him to fight the gang...
This bugtastic guide will give
you all the inside information
on what really happened when
one ant decided to fight back. But
first meet the heroes and villains of this
fANTastic story...

flik

Worker ant Flik is full of ideas. He dreams of a new, brighter colony, where the ants have machines to do all the work. However, most of his inventions go wrong, much to the irritation of the colony. Flik's desperation to impress the colony and the beautiful Princess Atta, whom he admires from afar, leads him to deceive them all. When Flik finds out that his 'warriors' are really circus bugs, his fear of failure makes him try to muddle through.

Flik befriends Princess Atta's younger sister, Dot. She is Flik's number one (make that only!) fan and fiercely defends him when the rest of the colony mock his ideas.

"For the colony and oppressed ants everywhere!"

Atta

Princess Atta is training to be queen. But she finds being in charge is hard work! When the grain offering is destroyed by Flik, Atta soon finds she has to do some swift talking to a very angry Hopper!
Atta wants Flik to keep out of the way, and sending him to find warrior bugs seems like the best way of ensuring he doesn't cause any more trouble. But when Flik returns with 'a bunch of clowns' she's furious — he wasn't supposed to actually **find** anyone! Atta thinks that fighting Hopper would be most 'unantly'.

"Queen training is hard work!"

HOPPER

Leader of the grasshopper gang,
Hopper is a big, scary, one-eyed grasshopper.
(He lost his right eye in a bird attack.)
Hopper forces the ant colony to supply
the gang's food and is not scared of anything
...except birds. He wants to keep the ant
colony in its place, so that he and his gang
never have to work
for their food.

"Let's ride."

Princess DoT

Dot is a tomboy. She likes playing with the older ants, but is often left behind because she can't fly! She is always told "not until your wings grow in" and dreams of the day when she can fly. A member of the Blueberry troop, Dot knows that teamwork gets things done—especially when it comes to defeating Hopper.

Dot's best friend is Flik. He explains to her that being little is not a bad thing. Dot thinks Flik's weird, but she still likes him.

"Not until my wings grow in!"

FLIK LEAVES ANT ISLAND IN FLAP!

BY EDNA GRUBB

WORKER ant Flik has hit the headlines yet again with his disastrous grain harvesting scheme which caused chaos at the annual grain offering.

As if endangering Princess Atta wasn't enough, he also placed our whole colony at risk by destroying our annual grain offering to Hopper and his gang.

Never before has the ant colony failed to supply the grasshoppers with their food but the unthinkable ha happened: somehow we have to supply Hopper with double the order by the tim the last leaf falls.

Winter food worry

But whether we can supply this, let alone find enough fo our own winter stores remains a big worry for the Ant Council.

The feeling is that Flik's big talk of tools and efficiency and improvements has gone

Flik photographed leaving the island

is in good hands!"

He is supported in his mission by Atta's younger sister, Princess Dot, who said, "He's going to find the bestest, roughest bugs you've ever seen."

The rest of us would be happier if the ant would stay away long enough for the new offering to be collected!

too far. Council member Cornelius commented, "I've survived eighty seasons without a new idea." This opinion is believed to be shared by the Ant Council, and no doubt explains their decision to send Flik away from Ant Island.

There is just one problem with this. Flik has had an idea to find bigger bugs to fight the grasshoppers.

When asked to comment Flik said, "Don't worry, the colony

Dot has faith in Flik

ATTA:
PRINCESS IN TRAINING

by **Antonia Larvae-Pupa,**
royal correspondent

Is beautiful Atta ready to be queen?

The recent visit by Hopper and his gang has prompted royal watchers to raise concerns over Princess Atta's readiness to become queen.

Never before has Hopper invaded the ant hill, and although Atta dealt with this problem to the best of her ability, my source tells me that it is felt that she may still need the back-up and experience of her mother, the Queen.

Princess Atta

The beautiful Princess does not seem to be able to make quick decisions – something she must learn to do if she is to become a true queen and leader of the colony.

She will need all the help we can give her to get through this difficult time. We must ensure that sudden difficulties of the Flik variety do not cause her any additional problems during our second harvest.

THE WORLD'S GREATEST

MYSTERY

Starring Manto the magnificent and his beautiful assistant Gypsy. Be intrigued as you watch the beautiful Gypsy disappear before your very eyes in the great magician's Chinese Cabinet of Metamorphosis!

LAUGHS!

The amazing clown trio, Heimlich, Slim and Francis' slapstick antics will have you rolling in the aisles!

IT'S CIRCUS TIME!

P. T. Flea's world famous Bug Circus is in town!
Book your tickets NOW to avoid disappointment
and come to see the most amazing show ever!
Hurry—we won't be here for ever...

TERROR!

Be scared out of your seat as our
fearless tamer, Rosie the spider,
faces ferocious Dim,
the terrifying monster beetle.

STUNTS!

Share the excitement of
our acrobatic team, Tuck
and Roll, as they perform
somersaults galore! Hey!

BUG CIRCUS

GREATEST

MYSTERY

Starring

beautiful

you w

b

The real mystery here is what has happened to Manny. His powers are fading and he is in too much of a mystic trance to notice! Poor Gypsy realises their act is past its best, but Manny doesn't take any notice of her.

Francis isn't a typical ladybird. For a start he's a BOY!
He never concentrates on clowning — he's too busy
getting into arguments when the circus audience
bug him with shouts of "Hey cutie!"
Slim the stick insect wants to be a proper actor.
But at the circus P. T. always casts him as a prop.
Heimlich the caterpillar hates performing on an
empty stomach. But since he's hungry all
the time, there's not much time to clown around.

IT'S CIRCUS TIME!

P. T. Flea

Book yo...
and ...
Hurry

P. T. has been in 'bugbiz' all his life. He can talk his way out of anything. But the little flea is frustrated by his bungling circus troupe and fires them before he's ruined. When 'Flaming Death' is a success, he wants his performers back. They may have hit the big time and there's money to be made!

COMING SOON TO A COLONY ... YOU!

TERROR!

Rosie is obsessed with spinning the perfect web. She is very fond of Dim and tends to mother him. Dim is not very bright, but he's lovable, and not at all terrifying!

... as our ... spider, ...etle.

STUNTS!

Share the excitement of our acrobatic team, Tuck and Roll, as they perform somersaults galore!

BUG CIRCUS

WANTED

Evil Hopper, leader of the grasshopper gang.
Crime: Terrorises ant colonies into supplying his gang with food.
Distinguishing Characteristics: Big, scary, one-eyed grasshopper.
Scared of nothing... except birds.
Favourite phrase: "The ants pick the food, the
grasshoppers eat the food."
Accomplices: Brother Molt, who leaves a trail
of skin wherever he goes. His wild henchman,
the vicious Thumper.
DO NOT approach this grasshopper.
He's extremely dangerous.

P. T. FLEA'S
GUIDE TO THE CIRCUS

"Roll-up, Roll-up ladies and gentlebugs for the magnificent P. T. Flea's guide to the circus..."

1. Any performer has to know his audience. Get them interested – give them the big schmooze.

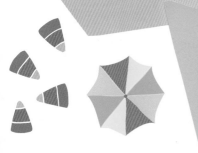

2. You have to get the audience's attention and keep it. This is called the 'art of showmanship'. I find that something along the lines of "I hold, in my hand, the match that decides whether two bugs live or die this very evening," does the trick.

3. Next you need drama and intrigue. For my world famous Flaming Death act, I laid a path of matches along the ring towards some flypaper. This keeps the audience on the edge of their wings.

4.
Organise your troupe. Use your 'able' assistants to show the audience what's going on. For Flaming Death, Tuck and Roll were my pill-bug cannon balls, Dim triggered the cannon, and as for Rosie, she had the most important job of all — spinning the safety net in fifteen seconds.

5.
Sounds good so far? OK, but in this bug-eat-bug world, the audience have seen it all before, so you gotta add in that something extra, to make them feel they're witnessing the most amazing thing ever. This is when you go for it. Tell them you'll do it BLINDFOLDED!

6.
Then pause to allow the tension to build up.

7. A true showman will do the following checks.
- Is your troupe disciplined?
- Have they practised their act?
- Most importantly, are they competent? Tuck and Roll were my downfall. They really know how to argue. The fighting duo fell on top of me. At this point the death-defying feat turned dangerous... I lit the match trail too soon, and worst of all Dim fired the cannon, knocking me towards the flypaper.

8. If things do go wrong, don't panic. As they say in bugbiz, the show must go on! Unfortunately, Rosie's web had a hole in it, and BAM! I went straight through the middle and onto the flypaper. Worse was to follow when BOOM! the flypaper went up!

9. This is the point where even a seasoned pro has to call it a day. A big failure means your troupe has to go – I fired all mine. It's tough at the top of bugbiz.

10. But you never know what will happen. Those bored flies, who'd seen it all in their 24-hour lives, loved my show. The act was famous! If your act is a hit, do a tour. After all, there's paying customers out there!

CITY EYE

BAR FLIES INJURED IN TIN-CAN DUST UP!

by Dee-Dee Longleggs

THE TIN-CAN bar will be closed until further notice, following a massive fight which took place late last night. The pitched battle involved many of the bar's customers, and resulted in large-scale damage to the building – most of it is believed to have happened when the bar tipped over. The fight began when a fly gang approached a group of out of town bugs and bullied a ladybird. Curiously, the bugs described themselves as the 'greatest warriors in the land' before the ladybird started the fight. One eyewitness said "It was mad! Things were flying all over the place – the bar tipped over, and when I came round I was stuck under a big

horsefly!"

The visiting bugs managed to slip away accompanied by a young ant. The ant, who said he was an inventor, had been hanging around asking the customers to help his colony.

FLAMING SUCCESS OR FLOP?

by S. Corpion *Entertainment critic*

'NOT A GOOD WAY to spend an evening when you've only got twenty-four hours to live' was what one member of the audience said after an evening at P. T. Flea's 'world famous' circus. Quite frankly I have to say that in all my seasons as an entertainment critic I have never seen such a shambolic second-rate performance – a view that was obviously shared by the dozens of flies that left halfway through the show. Lured by the opportunity to see a ferocious monster beetle, it was laughable to see the supposed 'monster' break down in tears when a blow from the beetle tamer's whip caught his foot. The clown act descended into chaos almost as soon as it started when the rather aggressive ladybird clown started a fight with some flies in the audience. Not so much ladybird as machobird...

However – the final act made up for sitting through the first few hours. P. T. Flea's 'Flaming Death' scene was a riot and made my evening out bearable.

For me the best part of all was seeing P.T. going up in smoke, and I have to say for such a chaotic early half, this one was a polished performance. The Flaming Death act looks like it will be a big hit – but there is one problem. P. T. Flea's performers have gone missing. Anyone with any information on their whereabouts is asked to contact P. T. Flea.

HEIMLICH'S food FILE

A caterpillar can never have enough food.
It is hard work preparing to be a butterfly,
and you should never work on an empty stomach.
My favourite food is leaves of all shapes and sizes.
But, in a crisis, anything will do.
I always find that during my circus act, a nice
piece of candy corn helps to focus the mind.
And anyway, it's too good for that fly audience
and their poo-poo hands! P. T. Flea always
complained that my appetite was eating into
his profits, but then as I always used to
tell him, one day I'll be a beautiful butterfly,
and then everything will be alright.
Here are some of my favourite recipes:

Heimlich's cabbage:

Take one large cabbage. Eat it.

Heimlich's three leaf salad:
Take three lettuce heads, tear off the leaves,
toss them in the air and eat them.

Slim's Guide
to being an
actor

I'd like to be able to share with you my guide to becoming the next big thing as far as acting goes. Unfortunately, P. T. insists that I be cast as a broom or a splinter, so I am still waiting for my big break. At the circus, anything went, as long as I was performing as a prop of some shape or form. I long for the smell of the greasepaint and the roar of the crowds, but in the clown act it was usually the flies that smelled, not the greasepaint! I dream of performing in some of the greatest plays in bugbiz. 'Caterpillar on a Hot Tin Roof' is a big favourite of mine. But until then I will have to be content with searching for a little spotlight to call my own.

Dot's Blueberry guide

The Blueberry Promise

I promise to be kind.
Brave. And the bestest
Blueberry I can be.
Always.

Remember:
- Teamwork all the way!
- Blueberries are bestest and toughest!
- Girls can do anything!
- If you're in trouble remember: Blueberry can-do will get you through!
- You don't have to wait for your wings to grow in to be a Blueberry.

Blueberry Rules
- You must always wear your Blueberry bandanna, and make sure it has spots added to it as a mark of respect to Francis, our honorary den mother.
- A Blueberry must always wear their leaf cape.

Blueberry badges will be awarded as follows:

membership badge

for teamwork

for outstanding bravery

WHAT'S BUGGING YOU?

You've heard about the characters in this amazing story. Now it's time to test your knowledge of **A Bug's Life** in this brain-boggling quiz that will bug you for hours!

1. Name the act that went so wrong it made P. T. Flea sack his circus troupe.

a. Flypaper Death
b. Flaming Death
c. Flaming Bugs

2. What's the name of the queen's pet?

a. Amoeba
b. Alfie
c. Aphie

3. Where does the ant colony live?

a. Ant Island
b. Ant Hill
c. Ant River

4. Which of Flik's inventions do we see first in the film?

a. a grain harvester
b. a telescope
c. a megaphone

6. How did Hopper lose his right eye?

a. He was in a bar fight.
b. A bird attacked him.
c. A bigger bug did it.

5. What happened to the ant colony's first food offering to Hopper's gang?

a. A bird ate it all.
b. The harvest failed.
c. Flik knocked the grain into the river bed.

7. What is the name of Hopper's brother?

a. Molt
b. Mort
c. Malt

8. What is the name of Hopper's henchman?
a. Killer
b. Thumper
c. Fluffy

9. When does Hopper say the gang will return to the anthill?
a. When the last leaf falls.
b. When they return from their holiday.
c. When the river starts flowing.

10. Which famous heroes do the circus bugs pretend to be when they fight the flies?
a. The Three Musketeers
b. Hercules
c. Robin Hood and his Merry Men

11. The ant colony's school performs a play for the 'warriors'. Can you name their teacher?
a. Mr Soil
b. Dr Flora
c. Thorny

12. When Francis and Dot are trapped by a bird where do they hide?

a. A crack in the river bed
b. The anthill
c. A hole in the tree on Ant Island

13. Where on Ant Island does the colony hide Flik's fake bird?

a. Under a pile of leaves
b. In the bird's nest with the real bird
c. In a knothole of Ant Island's tree

14. How does the Blueberry troop honour Francis for saving Dot?

a. They vote Francis 'Honorary Den Mother'.
b. They throw a party.
c. They give him a Blueberry badge.

15. How do the ants discover that the 'warriors' are actually circus performers?

a. Francis tells the Blueberries
b. Atta overhears Flik talking to them
c. P. T. Flea arrives and blows their cover

16. What is the circus bugs' parting gift to the ant colony?

a. A leaf
b. A seed
c. A rock

17. The circus bugs perform for Hopper, but who disappears in Manny's Chinese Cabinet of Metamorphosis?

a. Flik
b. The Queen
c. Dot

18. What causes Flik's fake bird to crash land?

a. P. T. Flea, a match and some lighter fluid
b. The wings fall off
c. It hits the tree

19. What happens to Hopper's brother, Molt, at the end of the film?

a. He joins the circus
b. He stays on Ant Island
c. He joins the Blueberrry troop

20. Who persuades Flik to go back to Ant Island to help the queen?

a. P. T. Flea
b. Atta
c. Dot

BUG BITES

Below are some of the best lines from the film, but can you remember who said them? To help you match the lines to the stars, here's a list of the characters with the number of lines each one has in this quiz.

1 "Not until my wings grow in."

2 "No more picking individual kernels. You can just cut down the entire stalk!"

3 "I'm never going to make a difference."

4 "Everything that made that giant tree is already contained in this tiny seed. All it needs is some time, a little bit of sunshine and rain..."

5 "You're weird. I like you!"

6 "Where's my FOOD?"

7 "Nature has a certain order. The sun grows the food, the ants pick the food, the grasshoppers eat the food."

8 "Let's ride!"

9 "We could send someone to get help!"

10 "Leave the island?"

11 "Don't worry. The colony is in good hands."

12 "He's going to get the bestest, roughest bugs you've ever seen."

13 "For the colony! And for oppressed ants everywhere!"

14 "No refunds after the first two minutes."

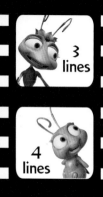
3 lines

4 lines

7 lines

3 lines

5 lines

3 lines

3 lines

3 lines

2 lines

15 "I hate performing on an empty stomach."

16 "You always cast me as the broom, the pole, the stick, a splinter..."

17 "Ooh! Candy corn! Let me help you finish it."

18 "So bein' a ladybird automatically makes me a **GIRL?**"

19 "Francis, leave the flies alone. They have poo-poo hands."

20 "Judging by your breath, you must have been buzzing round a dung heap all day."

21 "You're all fired!"

22 "Fired by a flea. How humiliating."

23 "Some day I will be a beautiful butterfly. Then everything will be better."

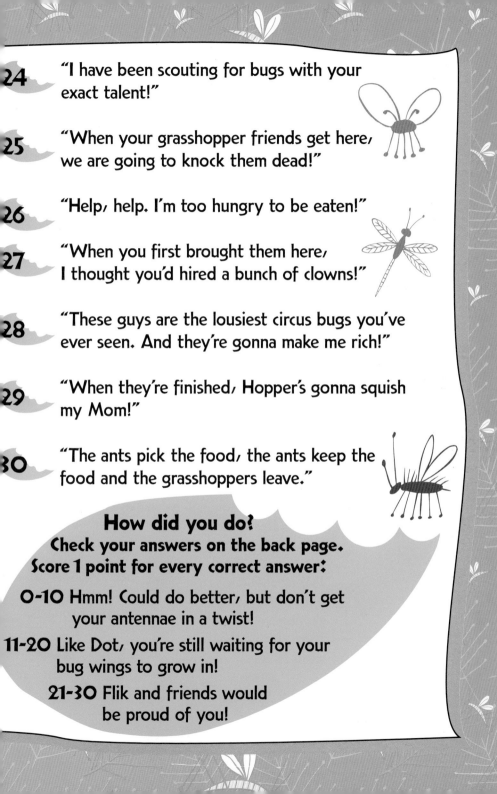

24 "I have been scouting for bugs with your exact talent!"

25 "When your grasshopper friends get here, we are going to knock them dead!"

26 "Help, help. I'm too hungry to be eaten!"

27 "When you first brought them here, I thought you'd hired a bunch of clowns!"

28 "These guys are the lousiest circus bugs you've ever seen. And they're gonna make me rich!"

29 "When they're finished, Hopper's gonna squish my Mom!"

30 "The ants pick the food, the ants keep the food and the grasshoppers leave."

How did you do?
Check your answers on the back page.
Score 1 point for every correct answer:

0-10 Hmm! Could do better, but don't get your antennae in a twist!

11-20 Like Dot, you're still waiting for your bug wings to grow in!

21-30 Flik and friends would be proud of you!

"Bugs are amazing creatures. Check out these mind-boggling facts..."

Insects don't have skeletons like human beings. Instead they have a hard outer shell casing. This is called an exoskeleton.

Insects have compound eyes which enable them to detect movement very easily.

Ants work collectively — there are males and workers, and soldiers, as well as the queen, who lays all the eggs.

Not all ants have wings. Worker ants don't have them — they don't need to fly.

Most of an ants' nest is underground and consists of a maze of tunnels.

Ants can live to an impressive age: the queen can live for up to 14 years, the worker ants for seven.

Ants have two jaws. The outer one is for carrying, and the inner one is for chewing. Soldier ants have bigger jaws to help them to defend their colony against intruders.

 Parasol ants grow their own food — a fungus which grows on leaves.

 Ants communicate using chemicals known as pheromones. They also use their antennae to tap out messages.

 Some insects, called termites build huge cone-like nests. In Africa these can grow up to 12 m high.

 Driver ants move their nests from place to place, picking up food on the way.

 Some bugs are nutritious and in parts of South America ants and grasshoppers are on the menu. In South-East Asia tarantulas are eaten and closer to home, in France, they eat snails. Yuk!

BUG JOKES

These bugtastic jokes
will have you
chuckling
away!

Waiter, waiter, there's
a spider in my soup.
-I know, Sir, it's
the fly's day off!

Did you hear about
the squashed glow-worm?
-He was de-lighted!

What's the smallest
ant in the world?
-An inf-ant!

What's the difference between
a coyote and a flea?
-One howls on the prairie and
the other prowls on the hairy!

What's the
biggest moth
of all?
-A mammoth!

What insect is musical?
- A humbug!

Where do tadpoles
change into frogs?
-In the croakroom!

Where do spiders play football?
-Webley stadium!

 Two flies on a coffee cup.
Which one loses its patience first?
-The one that flies off the handle!

What happens
when you cross
an anthill with
some seeds?
-You get ants
in your plants!

 What did the earwig say when
he fell off the wall?
-Ear-wig-go, Ear-wig-go,
Ear-wig-go!

 Why was the insect arrested?
-For being a litter bug!

 Knock
knock.
Who's there?
Amos
Amos who?
A mosquito!

What do ants take
when they're ill?
-Ant-ibiotics!

 What goes croak croak
when it's foggy?
-A Froghorn!

 What's black and hairy and
goes up and down?
-A tarantula in a lift!

WHICH BUG ARE YOU?

Are you more like Dot, Atta, or Flik? Find out with this quick quiz.

1. You have a project to do for school. Do you:
a. Invent a machine to do your project?
b. Get your classmates together and do the project as a team?
c. Find that your teacher trusts you to help your friends with their projects?

2. When you are older, would you rather be:
a. An inventor?
b. An adventurer?
c. Prime Minister?

3. Which of these describes you:
a. Bright ideas start here
b. Teamwork all the way
c. A leader

4. What do your friends think of you? (Be honest!)

a. You are a bit wacky, but very imaginative.

b. You are tough, but you'll stand up for your friends.

c. You are kind, but not afraid of being in charge.

5. Which of these do you think is most important:

a. Being imaginative.

b. Being brave.

c. Being liked by everyone.

FLIK

Mostly a's
You are like Flik, imaginative and full of ideas, but they might not always work out.

DoT

Mostly b's
You are like Princess Dot — you may be small but your motto is teamwork!

Atta

Mostly c's
You are like Atta, you like being in charge, in fact some would say you're a born leader!

Essential BUG TERMS

ANT ISLAND - The home of Flik and the ant colony.

BLUEBERRIES - The name of Dot's scout troop.

BIRD - Flik builds a fake bird. Hopper is afraid of them.

CIRCUS - The bugs perform in P. T. Flea's circus.

CITY - Flik goes there to find some big tough bugs to help the colony to defeat Hopper.

DOUBLE THE ORDER - Hopper demands this when he finds out his food offering is missing.

EYE - Hopper lost his right eye in a fight with a bird.

FLAMING DEATH - P.T.'s world famous act, that eventually becomes a success.

GRAIN HARVESTER - Flik's labour saving invention.

IDEAS - Flik has loads of ideas, but the colony views them with suspicion.

OFFERING STONE - The ants pile Hopper's food offering onto this big flat stone.

SPARROW - An encounter with this monster bird gives Flik the idea of building a fake bird.

TELESCOPE - Made from a dewdrop and a rolled up leaf, this is Flik's first gift to Dot.

UNTIL THE LAST LEAF FALLS - The length of time the colony has to collect Hopper's food.

WARRIORS - Flik thinks the circus bugs are fighters!

WINGS - Dot is waiting for hers to grow in.

Answers

WHAT'S BUGGING YOU QUIZ

1. b	2. c
3. a	4. a
5. c	6. b
7. a	8. b
9. a	10. c
11. a	12. a
13. c	14. a
15. c	16. c
17. b	18. a
19. a	20. c

BUG BITES

1. Dot
2. Flik
3. Flik
4. Flik
5. Dot
6. Hopper

7. Hopper
8. Hopper
9. Flik
10. Atta
11. Flik
12. Dot
13. Flik
14. P. T. Flea

15. Heimlich
16. Slim
17. Heimlich
18. Francis
19. Heimlich
20. Francis

21. P. T. Flea
22. Slim
23. Heimlich
24. Flik
25. Francis

26. Heimlich
27. Atta
28. P. T. Flea
29. Dot
30. Atta